Hey, Diddle Diddle

and other nonsense Rhymes

Illustrated by Da...

Published by

THE TOON STUDIO™
OF BEVERLY HILLS

D1511392

ONE, TWO, THREE

One, two, three, four, five,
Once I caught a fish alive.
Six, seven, eight, nine, ten,
But I let it go again.
Why did you let it go?
Because it bit my finger so.
Which finger did it bite?
The little one upon the right.

3

THE CAT AND THE FIDDLE

Hey, diddle, diddle!
The cat and the fiddle,
The cow jumped over the moon;
The little dog laughed
To see such sport,
And the dish ran away with the spoon.

JUST LIKE ME

"I went up one pair of stairs."
"Just like me."

"I went up two pairs of stairs."
"Just like me."

"I went into a room."
"Just like me."

"I looked out of a window."
"Just like me."

"And there I saw a monkey."
"Just like me."

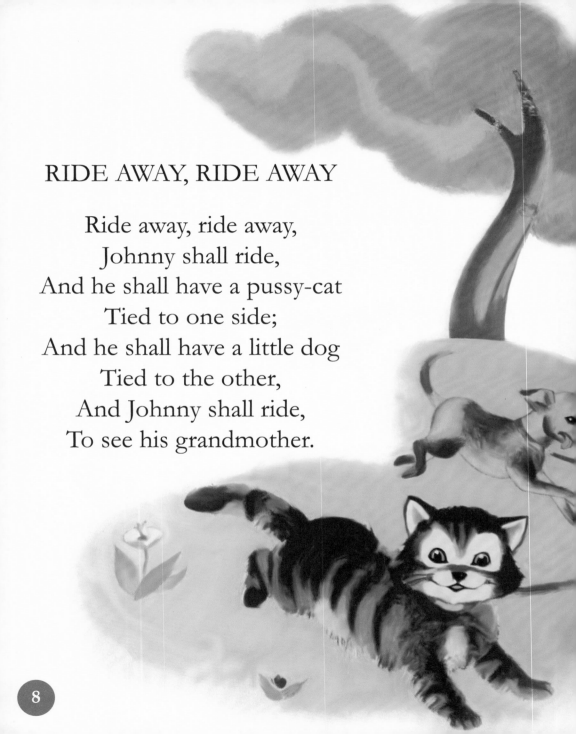

RIDE AWAY, RIDE AWAY

Ride away, ride away,
Johnny shall ride,
And he shall have a pussy-cat
Tied to one side;
And he shall have a little dog
Tied to the other,
And Johnny shall ride,
To see his grandmother.

TWEEDLE-DUM AND TWEEDLE-DEE

Tweedle-dum and Tweedle-dee
Resolved to have a battle,
For Tweedle-dum said Tweedle-dee
Had spoiled his nice new rattle.

Just then flew by a monstrous crow,
As big as a tar barrel,
Which frightened both the heroes so,
They quite forgot their quarrel.

IF WISHES WERE HORSES

If wishes were horses,
beggars would ride.
If turnips were watches,
I would wear one by my side.
And if "ifs" and "ands"
Were pots and pans
There'd be no work for tinkers!

11

THE MAN OF BOMBAY

There was a fat man of Bombay,
Who was smoking one sunshiny day;
When a bird called a snipe
Flew away with his pipe,
Which vexed the fat man of Bombay.

PUSSY-CAT AND QUEEN

"Pussy-cat, pussy-cat,
Where have you been?"
"I've been to London
To look at the Queen."

"Pussy-cat, pussy-cat,
What did you there?"
"I frightened a little mouse
Under the chair."

BANBURY CROSS

Ride a cock-horse to Banbury Cross,
To see an old lady upon a white horse.
Rings on her fingers, and bells on her toes,
She shall have music wherever she goes.

DUCKS AND DRAKES

A duck and a drake,
And a halfpenny cake,
With a penny to pay the old baker.
A hop and a scotch
Is another notch
Slitherum, slatherum, take her.

THE GIRL IN THE LANE

The girl in the lane,
that couldn't speak plain,
Cried, "Gobble, gobble, gobble."
The man on the hill
that couldn't stand still
Went hobble, hobble, hobble.

LOCK AND KEY

"I am a gold lock."
"I am a gold key."
"I am a silver lock."
"I am a silver key."
"I am a brass lock."
"I am a brass key."
"I am a lead lock."
"I am a lead key."
"I am a don lock."
"I am a don key."

COCK-A-DOODLE-DO!

Cock-doodle-do!
My dame has lost her shoe,
My master's lost his fiddle-stick
And knows not what to do.

Cock-doodle-do!
What is my dame to do?
Till master finds his fiddle-stick,
She'll dance without her shoe.

PUSSY-CAT AND THE DUMPLINGS

Pussy-cat ate the dumplings, the dumplings,
Pussy-cat ate the dumplings.
Mamma stood by, and cried, "Oh fie!
Why did you eat the dumplings?"